A Year on the Farm

By Sue Unstead

Series Editor Deborah Lock
Art Editor Yamini Panwar
Pre-production Editor Francesca Wardell
DTP Designer Anita Yadav, Syed Md Farhan
Picture Researcher Sumedha Chopra
Managing Editor Soma B. Chowdhury
Managing Art Editor Ahlawat Gunjan
Art Director Martin Wilson

Reading Consultant Shirley Bickler

First published in Great Britain by
Dorling Kindersley Limited
80 Strand, London, WC2R 0RL

Copyright © 2015 Dorling Kindersley Limited
A Penguin Random House Company
10 9 8 7 6 5 4 3 2 1
001—271660—June/2015

A CIP catalogue record for this book is available from the British Library.

ISBN: 978-0-2411-8278-9

Printed and bound in China
The publisher would like to thank the following for their kind permission
to reproduce their photographs:
(Key: a-above; b-below/bottom; c-centre; f-far; l-left; r-right; t-top)
1 Alamy Images: Tatiana Cahill. **7 Getty Images:** Digital Vision. **8 iStockphoto.com:** RMAX (b). **9 Getty Images:** Image
Source (r). **10–11 Getty Images:** E+/Jason Titzer (b). **12 Getty Images:** Duncan Davis (br); E+/stocknshares (clb). **13 Getty
Images:** Mattias Nilsson (clb); Ronnie Kaufman/Larry Hirshowitz (br). **14 iStockphoto.com:** JacobH (t, b). **15 iStockphoto.com:**
JacobH (t, b). **17 Fotolia:** Olena Pantiukh (bc). **19 Corbis:** Cultura/Monty Rakusen (tr). **20 iStockphoto.com:** TheBusman (tl).
21 Dreamstime.com: Orangesquid (cra); Sarah Theophilus (cb); **iStockphoto.com:** martin_33 (crb). **22 Corbis:** Image Source/
Sebastian Marmaduke (cla). **24–25 Dorling Kindersley:** The Cotswold Farm Park, Gloucestershire (b). **24 iStockphoto.com:**
RMAX. **25 123RF.com:** Francisco De Casa Gonzalez (tr). **26 iStockphoto.com:** ilfede (tl). **26–27 Getty Images:** Vetta/
George Clerk (c). **27 Getty Images:** Visuals Unlimited, Inc./Nigel Cattlin (bl). **28–29 Dreamstime.com:** Mike_kiev (b).
29 Corbis: Cultura / Hybrid Images (r). **30 123RF.com:** martinak (cb/Butter); Sergey Mironov (crb); **Alamy Images:** Valentyn
Volkov (cl); **Dreamstime.com:** Robyn Mackenzie (clb); **iStockphoto.com:** vikif (cb/yoghurt). **31 iStockphoto.com:** Lauri
Patterson (clb). **32–33 123RF.com:** Jean-Pierre Chretien (b). **33 iStockphoto.com:** tankist276 (c). **34–35 Alamy Images:**
Chris Pancewicz. **35 Alamy Images:** imageBROKER/Hartmut Pöstges (br). **36 iStockphoto.com:** jorgeantonio (tl).
36–37 Dreamstime.com: Marcomayer (b). **38 123RF.com:** jahmaica (cb); **iStockphoto.com:** pkripper503 (cla).
39 123RF.com: Karol Czinege (tl); Vitaly Suprun (ca); Norman Kin Hang Chan (clb); **Photolibrary:** Digital Vision/
Akira Kaede (crb). **42 123RF.com:** Alexey Zarodov (bl); sauletas (crb); **Alamy Images:** Chris Pancewicz (cla)
Jacket images: Front: **Dorling Kindersley:** Lister Wilder b. Fotolia: Vadim Yerofeyev ca.
Spine: Corbis: Peter Mason / cultura.
All other images © Dorling Kindersley
For further information see: www.dkimages.com

Contents

Our Farm
Welcome to the farm!

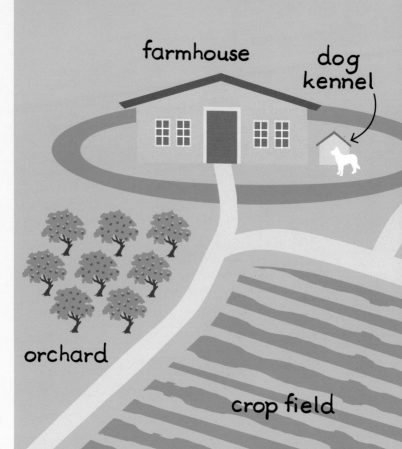

farmhouse

dog kennel

orchard

crop field

4

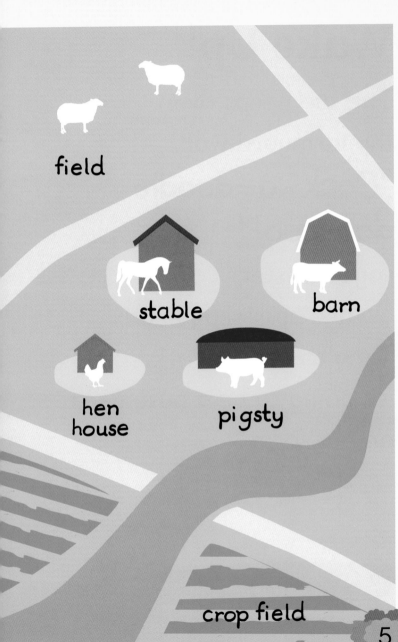

field

stable

barn

hen
house

pigsty

crop field

5

Wake Up!

The sun peeps over
the farmyard wall.
**"Cock-a-doodle
dooooooo!"**
says Rooster.
"Wake up, sleepy heads.
Time to get to work.
It's going to be a busy year
on our farm."

Cock-a-doodle doooooo!

7

Chapter 1
Winter

"Oh dear,"
says Mrs Farmer,
"I don't like these
dark mornings."

"Come on, Shep,"
she calls to her dog.
"Let's go and collect
some eggs
for breakfast.
Now where have
the silly hens
laid their eggs?"
Shep wags his tail.

9

Mr Farmer and Red Tractor
are already out on the farm.

Chug, chug, chug…
crunch, splash, splosh.

It is cold and frosty
up on the hill.

Today it is time to get
the fields ready.
Up and down they go,
churning up the soil.

All day Red Tractor
works in the field,
turning over the soil.

"What a long day!"
says Mr Farmer.
"Time to head home and
put the animals to bed."
The horses are in the stable.
The noisy pigs are in their sty.
The cows are in the barn.
Rooster and the hens are
in the hen house.

Seasons

These pictures show how a farm changes through the year. What differences do you see?

Winter

Spring

14

Summer

Autumn

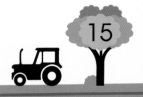

15

Chapter 2
Spring

"You can tell it's spring,"
says Mrs Farmer.
"All the animals are so busy
with their babies!"

Cheep–cheep!

"Cluck, cluck, cluck,"
says Hen.
"Look at my new chicks!"
Six fluffy balls of yellow
feathers run behind her.
"Cheep-cheep," they cry.

"Baa, baa."
There are four woolly lambs
inside the barn.
"Where's our maaamaaa?"
they bleat.
One little lamb is lying
in the straw.

Baa, baa!

Mrs Farmer picks it up.
She feeds it milk from a bottle.
"You will soon grow strong,"
she says.

Red Tractor is taking hay
to the horses out in the field.
A foal is trying out
its wobbly legs.

20

Now it is time to plant seed
in the fields:
potatoes in
the little field,
wheat in
the big field
and peas
by the stream.

Who Am I?

Match the animals to the clues.

piglet

kid

lamb

foal

calf

1. **Baaa!** My mum is an ewe.
   My dad is a ram. Who am I?

2. **Oink oink!** My mum is a sow.
   My dad is a boar. Who am I?

3. **Maaaa!** My mum is a nanny.
   My dad is a billy. Who am I?

4. **Neigh neigh!** My mum is a
   mare. My dad is a stallion.
   Who am I?

5. **Moo!** My mum is a cow.
   My dad is a bull. Who am I?

1. Lamb; 2. Piglet; 3. Kid;
4. Foal; 5. Calf.

23

Chapter 3
Summer

It is summertime.
Mr Farmer, Shep and
Red Tractor go out
to the fields.

It is time to round up
the sheep.
"Let's get those
woolly coats clipped,"
says Mr Farmer.
"You will be far too hot
in the sun."

Mr Farmer has
lots of jobs to do.
First he goes down
to the stream
to spray the peas.
Spit, sprit, spritzzzz.

Next he waters the potatoes.
Whoosh, whoosh.

Then Red Tractor helps him
to cut the grass
to make hay.
**Chip, chop,
chippety chop.**

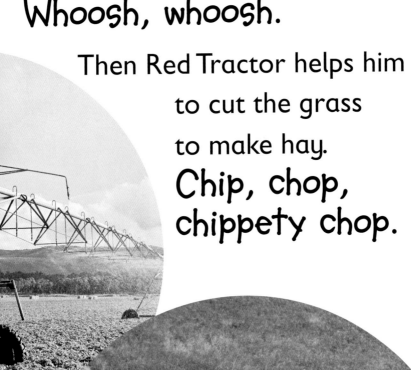

"Moo," says Cow.
"I could munch
this tasty grass all day."
"Time for milking,"
says Mr Farmer.

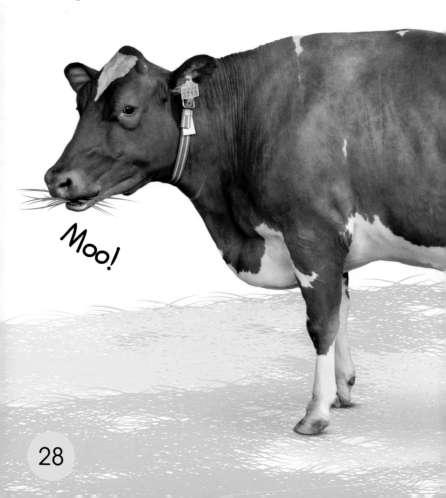

Moo!

"What lovely creamy milk,"
says Mrs Farmer.
"We shall make
some butter and
some cheese."

Food from the Farm

Farms give us many different foods.

Dairy cows give us milk to drink.
Milk can also be turned into these dairy foods.

Eggs come from hens.

cream

butter

cheese

yoghurt

Wheat is made into flour for bread.

peas

potatoes

apples

31

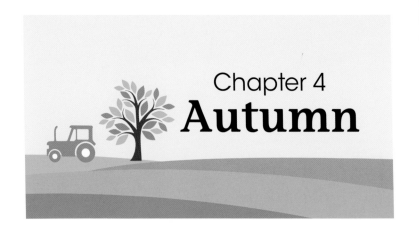

Chapter 4
Autumn

Mr Farmer and Red Tractor
go up to the big field
every day.
"Let's see if this wheat
is ready," he says.

He picks a stalk and
rubs the grain in his fingers.
"It's time to cut the wheat.
Let's fetch Combine Harvester."

Combine Harvester and
Red Tractor work
in the field all day long.
Swish, swish.

The stalks of wheat are cut as Combine Harvester drives through them.

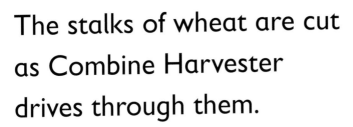

Whoosh, whoosh.
The seeds of grain fall into the hopper.

Roly-poly.
The stalks are rolled into bales of straw.

Mrs Farmer picks the apples
in the orchard.
"Now I shall make
an apple pie for tea."

Mr Farmer brings in a box
of potatoes and peas.
The harvest is in.
The hay is in the barn.
Zzzz.
Mr and Mrs Farmer sleep.
They are too tired to finish
their apple pie.

Farms Around the World

Corn plants
Corn is used in cooking oil and cornflour.

Bananas
Bananas grow on trees in plantations.

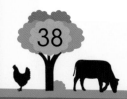

38

Sunflowers
Sunflower seeds make cooking oil.

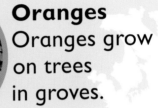

Oranges
Oranges grow on trees in groves.

Cacao trees
Cocoa beans are made into chocolate.

Rice paddy
Rice grows in flooded fields.

39

Let's Grow Potatoes

You will need:

- seed potatoes, sprouting
- very large pot with holes and small stones in the bottom
- soil
- water and plant food

1 Half-fill the pot with soil. Place five potatoes just below the soil with shoots upwards.

2 Each time the shoots appear, cover with more soil until the pot is full.

3 Keep the soil well watered, remove weeds and add plant food every few weeks.

4 Either pull up the potatoes when the plant flowers; or let the leaves die back to have bigger potatoes.

41

Farm Tractors

Each kind of tractor is useful for doing a different job.

Plough
Tractors with ploughs churn up the soil.

Sprayer
Tractors with sprayers water the plants.

Baler
Tractors with balers press crops into bales.

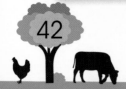

Farm Quiz

1. Where on the farm do the pigs live?

2. What did Mrs Farmer collect from the hens?

3. Which baby's dad is a bull?

4. What happens to sheep's woolly coats in the summer?

5. Name two things milk can be made into.

Answers on page 45.

Glossary

churn turn and mix

dairy foods made from milk

hay dried grass

hopper this holds the seeds
of wheat (grain)

orchard place where
fruit trees grow

plantation large group of
the same kind of plant

stalk tall part of a plant

straw dried stalks of grain

Index

Answers to the Farm Quiz:
1. Pigsty; **2.** Eggs; **3.** Calf;
4. They get clipped;
5. Check answer on page 30.

Guide for Parents

DK Reads is a three-level interactive reading adventure series for children, developing the habit of reading widely for both pleasure and information. These chapter books have an exciting main narrative interspersed with a range of reading genres to suit your child's reading ability. Each book is designed to develop your child's reading skills, fluency, grammar awareness, and comprehension in order to build confidence and engagement when reading.

Ready for a *Beginning to Read* book

YOUR CHILD SHOULD

- be using phonics, including consonant blends, such as bl, gl and sm, to read unfamiliar words; and common word endings, such as plurals, ing, ed and ly.

- be using the storyline, illustrations and the grammar of a sentence to check and correct his/her own reading.

- be pausing briefly at commas, and for longer at full stops; and altering his/her expression to respond to question, exclamation and speech marks.

A VALUABLE AND SHARED READING EXPERIENCE

For many children, reading requires much effort but adult participation can make this both fun and easier. So here are a few tips on how to use this book with your child.

TIP 1 Check out the contents together before your child begins:

- read the text about the book on the back cover.

- read through and discuss the contents page together to heighten your child's interest and expectation.

- make use of unfamiliar or difficult words on the page in a brief discussion.

- chat about the non-fiction reading features used in the book, such as headings, captions, recipes, lists or charts.

TIP 2 Support your child as he/she reads the story pages:

- give the book to your child to read and turn the pages.

- where necessary, encourage your child to break a word into syllables, sound out each one and then flow the syllables together. Ask him/her to reread the sentence to check the meaning.

- when there's a question mark or an exclamation mark, encourage your child to vary his/her voice as he/she reads the sentence. Demonstrate how to do this if it is helpful.

TIP 3 Praise, share and chat:

- the factual pages tend to be more difficult than the story pages, and are designed to be shared with your child.

- ask questions about the text and the meaning of the words used. These help to develop comprehension skills and awareness of the language used.

A FEW ADDITIONAL TIPS

- Try and read together everyday. Little and often is best. These books are divided into manageable chapters for one reading session. However after 10 minutes, only keep going if your child wants to read on.

- Always encourage your child to have a go at reading difficult words by themselves. Praise any self-corrections, for example, "I like the way you sounded out that word and then changed the way you said it, to make sense."

- Read other books of different types to your child just for enjoyment and information.

Series consultant **Shirley Bickler** is a longtime advocate of carefully crafted, enthralling texts for young readers. Her LIFT initiative for infant teaching was the model for the National Literacy Strategy Literacy Hour, and she is co-author of *Book Bands for Guided Reading* published by Reading Recovery based at the Institute of Education.

Have you read these other great books from DK?

BEGINNING TO READ

Holly's dream has come true – she gets her very own puppy.

Play hide and seek with the bugs. Can you spot them?

Hard hats on! Watch the busy machines build a new school.

STARTING TO READ ALONE

Discover life in a medieval castle during peacetime and war.

Join David on an amazing trip to meet elephants in Asia and Africa.

Embark on a mission to explore the solar system. First stop – Mars.

FIRST PUBLISHED 2014

Special thanks to Madame Grant, Monsieur Garton & Madame
O'Connor for their editorial assistance

First Edition